Fantastic everyday Phonics practice from CGP!

CGP's Daily Practice Books are brilliant for building Phonics skills all the way through Reception — there's a mixed practice exercise for every day of the year.

What's more, they follow the National Curriculum 'Letters and Sounds' programme, so you can be sure they cover everything children need to learn.

This book is for the **Summer Term** of **Reception**.
It covers **Phase 4** of the 'Letters and Sounds' programme, including:

- **Adjacent consonants** such as **cr**, **sk**, **st**, **nd**, **lt** and **nch**

- More **tricky words**

What CGP is all about

Our sole aim here at CGP is to produce the highest quality books
— carefully written, immaculately presented and
dangerously close to being funny.

Then we work our socks off to get them out to you
— at the cheapest possible prices.

Contents

☑ Use the tick boxes to help keep a record of which tests have been attempted.

Published by CGP

ISBN: 978 1 78908 480 1

Written by Juliette Green

Editors: Daniel Fielding, Rebecca Greaves, Christopher Lindle, Sam Norman
Reviewer: Clare Leck

With thanks to Rosa Roberts and Lucy Towle for the proofreading.

Images throughout the book from www.edu-clips.com.

Printed by Elanders Ltd, Newcastle upon Tyne.
Based on the classic CGP style created by Richard Parsons.

How to Use this Book

This book is for children to complete in the Reception <u>Summer Term</u>. Each page looks like this:

The book is split into <u>12 weeks</u>, with <u>5 days per week</u>.

The box at the top of the page contains <u>instructions</u>. Read through these with your child and go through the <u>worked example</u> so they know what they're meant to do.

You will need to read through the instructions for any <u>extension activities</u>.

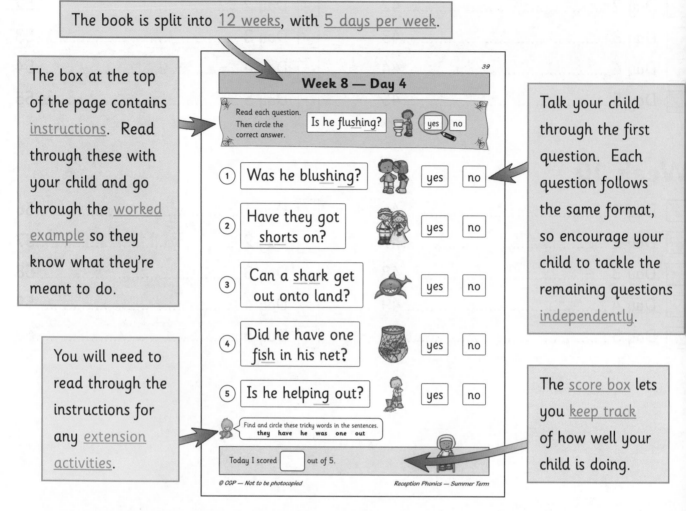

Talk your child through the first question. Each question follows the same format, so encourage your child to tackle the remaining questions <u>independently</u>.

The <u>score box</u> lets you <u>keep track</u> of how well your child is doing.

This book requires your child to <u>match pictures to words</u>.
You may need to help your child <u>identify</u> some pictures they're not sure of.

Phonics Hints for Helpers

Familiarise yourself with the <u>features</u> of this book below before you begin:

- <u>Word frames</u> are used in spelling and writing activities. There is one box for each <u>sound</u>. A sound can consist of more than one letter.

c	oa	l

- A <u>grey line</u> under two or more letters in a word is a reminder that these letters work together to make one sound.

bright<u>er</u>

- <u>Tricky words</u> are words with letters that have a sound that does not correspond to the expected sound, or that have a sound that has not yet been learned. Tricky words are written into <u>blue boxes</u>.

she   be

was

Week 1 — Day 1

Say the word, then add a letter to the **end** to make a new word that matches the picture.

Choose from these letters:

d   k   p   t

men → | m | e | n | d |

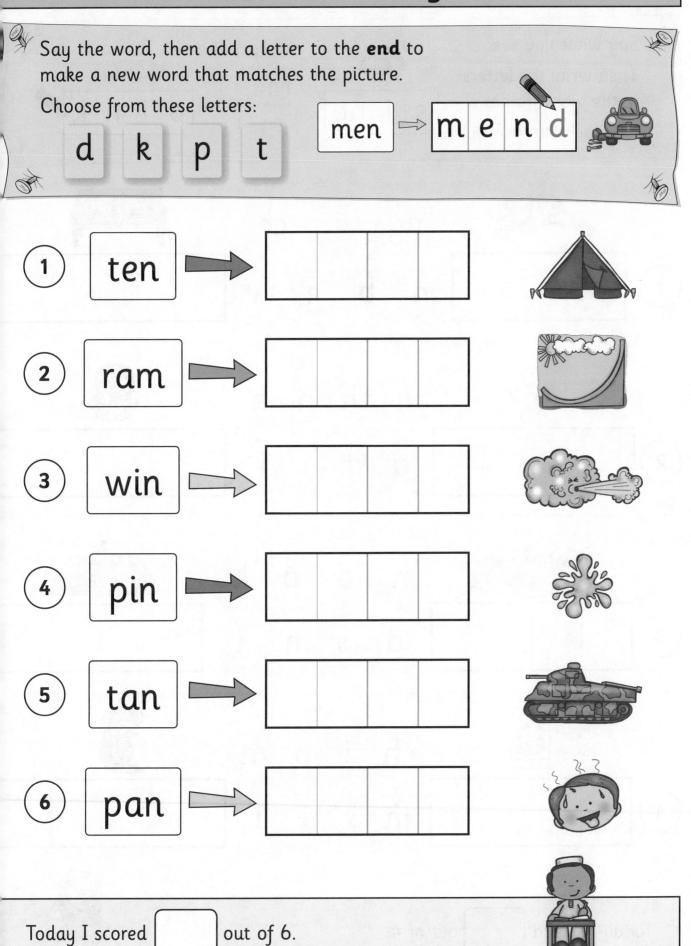

1   ten →

2   ram →

3   win →

4   pin →

5   tan →

6   pan →

Today I scored [ ] out of 6.

Reception Phonics — Summer Term

Week 1 — Day 2

Say what you see.
Then write the letters in the word frames.
Use each letter once.

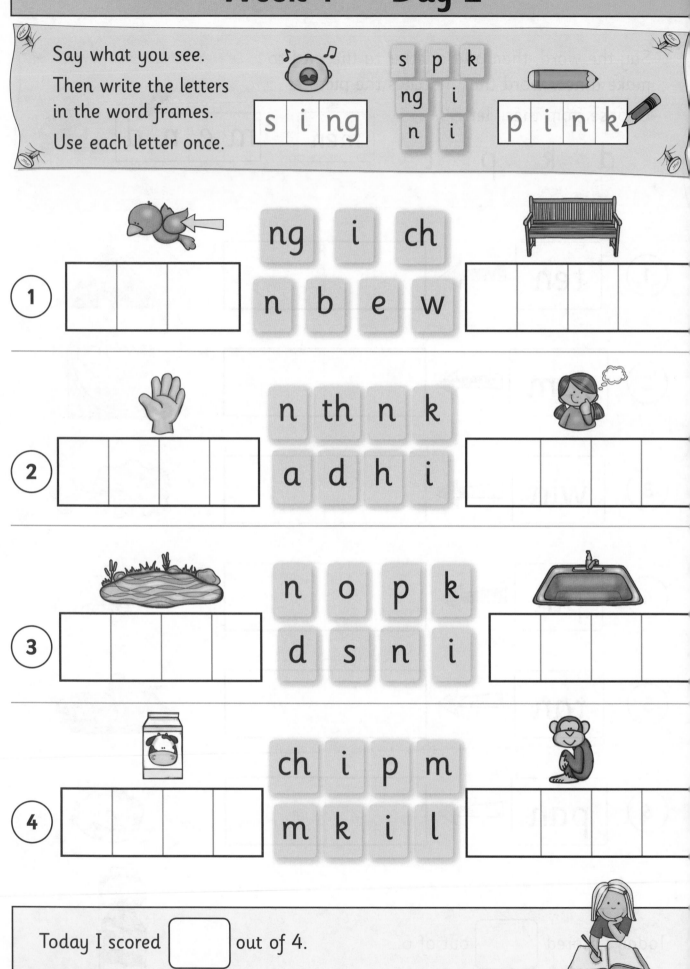

s | i | ng

s p k
ng   i
n   i

p | i | n | k

1

ng i ch
n b e w

2

n th n k
a d h i

3

n o p k
d s n i

4

ch i p m
m k i l

Today I scored ☐ out of 4.

Week 1 — Day 3

Copy one of the words to complete the sentence.

Can | he | help us?

me   we   be   he

1. This is _____.

2. Is _____ in a band?

3. I must _____ good.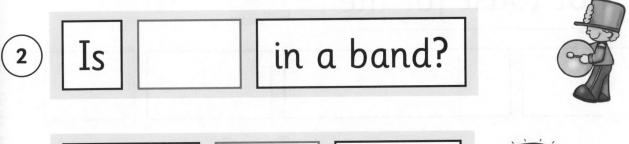

4. Kel will _____ a bee.

5. Can _____ jump high?

Today I scored [ ] out of 5.

Reception Phonics — Summer Term

Week 1 — Day 4

Write the caption or sentence into the word frames.

Camp with me.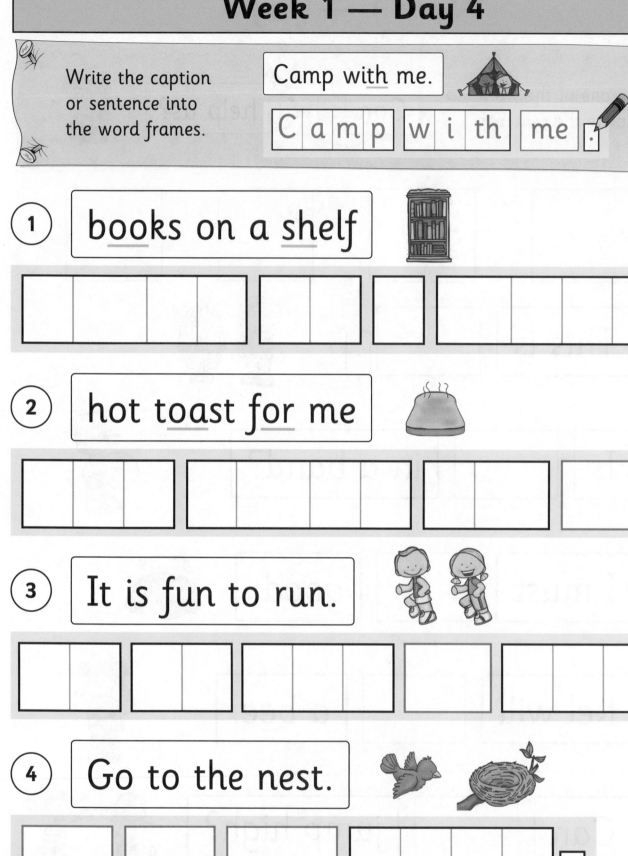

| C | a | m | p | | w | i | th | | me | . |

1 books on a sh**el**f

2 hot t**oa**st **f**or me

3 It is fun to run.

4 Go to the nest.

Today I scored [ ] out of 4.

Week 1 — Day 5

Circle the picture that matches the sentence.  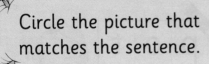 | The rock is so h<u>ard</u>. |

1  | She said she is the best at golf. |

2  | He felt so damp. |

3 | He said it was hot. |

4 | He had to p<u>u</u>ll the dog so har<u>d</u>. |

5 | He said it was t<u>oo</u> ti<u>gh</u>t. |

 Find and circle these words in the sentences.
said   **so**
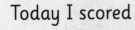

Today I scored [ ] out of 5.

Reception Phonics — Summer Term

Week 2 — Day 1

Say the word. Then add a letter to the **start** to make a word that matches the picture.

pot ➡ s p o t

Choose from these letters:

s g t

1 pin ➡ [| | |]

2 win ➡ [| | |]

3 ran ➡ [| | |]

4 lad ➡ [| | |]

5 weep ➡ [| | |]

6 tick ➡ [| | |]

Today I scored [   ] out of 6.

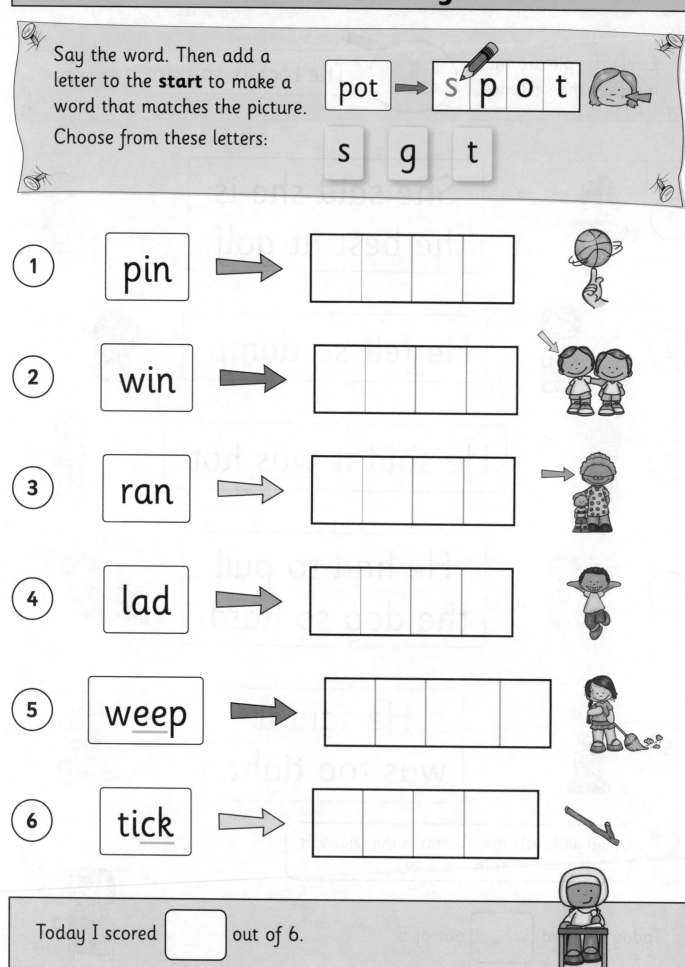

Week 2 — Day 2

Say what you see.
Then write the letters
in the word frames.
Use each letter once.

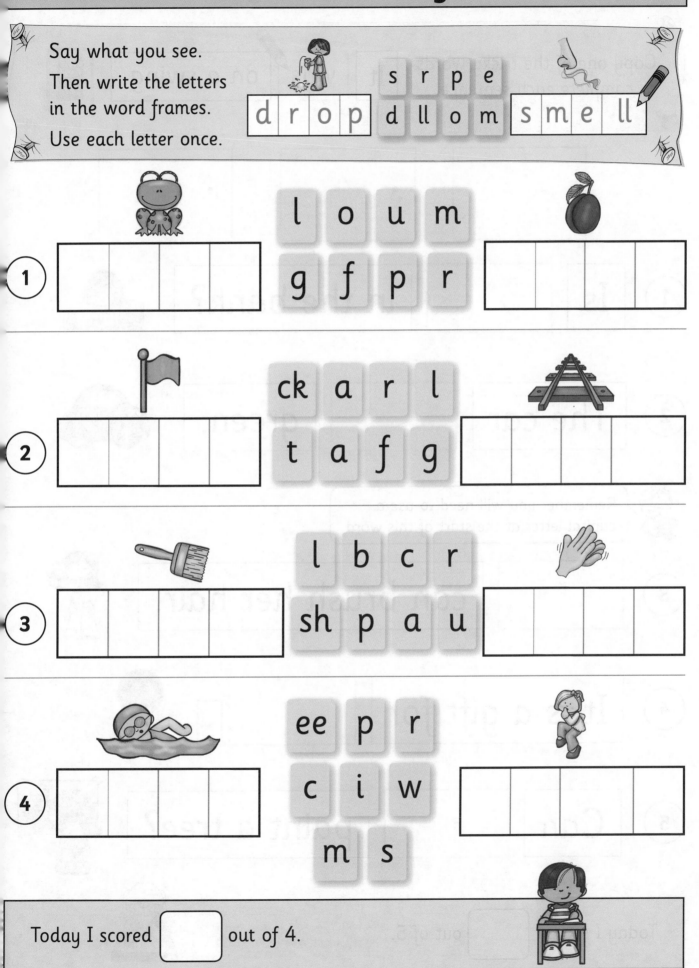

| d | r | o | p |

s r p e
d ll o m

| s | m | e | ll |

1 frog: l o u m / g f p r — plum

2 flag: ck a r l / t a f g — track

3 brush: l b c r / sh p a u — clap

4 swim: ee p r / c i w m s — sleep

Today I scored ☐ out of 4.

Week 2 — Day 3

Copy one of the tricky words to complete each sentence.

It | was | on a swing.

she | was | you

1 Is ____ in the bank?

2 The car ____ green.

Remember you will need to use a capital letter at the start of this word.

3 ____ can brush her hair.

4 It is a gift for ____ .

5 Can ____ paint a tree?

Today I scored ____ out of 5.

Week 2 — Day 4

Write each sentence in the word frames.

We can turn.

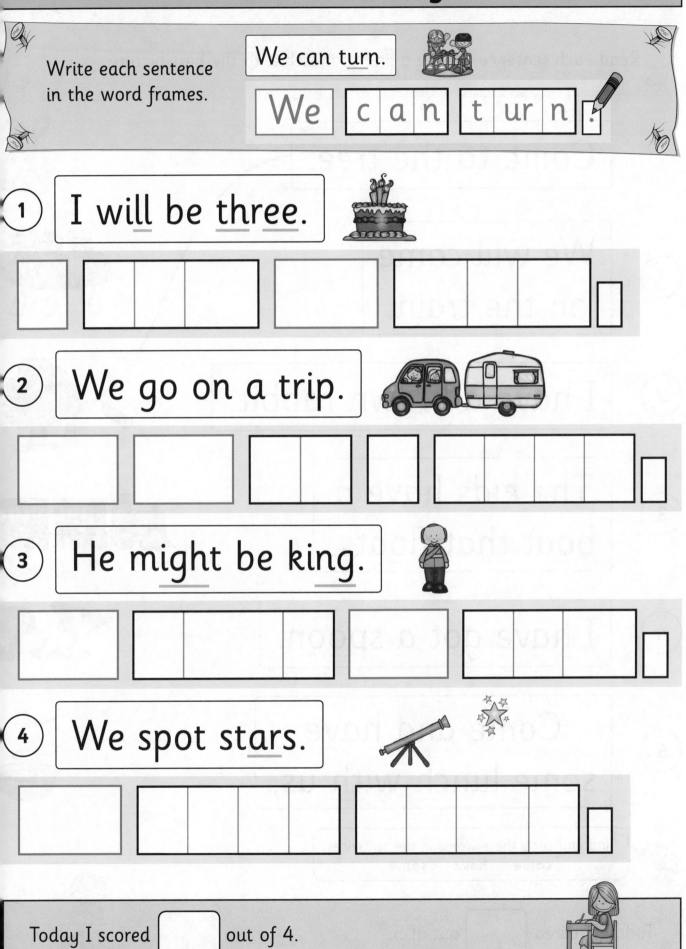

We c a n t u r n .

1 I will be three.

2 We go on a trip.

3 He might be king.

4 We spot stars.

Today I scored [ ] out of 4.

Reception Phonics — Summer Term

Week 2 — Day 5

Read each sentence. Draw a line to match it to the best picture.

Come to the tree.

1 We will come
on the train.

2 I have a brown rabbit.

3 The kids have a
boat that floats.

4 I have got a spoon.

5 Come and have
some lunch with us.

 Find and circle these words in the sentences.
come   have   some

Today I scored [   ] out of 5.

Week 3 — Day 1

Add the letters to the start **and** end of the word.
Then write the new word.

1. s + tan + d

2. t + run + k

3. d + ran + k

4. c + run + ch

5. th + an + k

Today I scored ☐ out of 5.

Reception Phonics — Summer Term

Week 3 — Day 2

Sound out each word. Colour the best picture to match the word.

stamp

1 plump

2 shrink

3 spring

4 blend

5 strong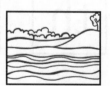

6 street

Today I scored [   ] out of 6.

Week 3 — Day 3

Say what you see. Then write the letters in the word frames.

p	r			s	p	r	ai	n
ai	s	n						

1 k n u k s

2 ng i r t s

3 p n i t r s

4 p c s a r s

5 ff u r c s

Today I scored ☐ out of 5.

Reception Phonics — Summer Term

Week 3 — Day 4

Write each sentence in the word frames.

He slept on a desk.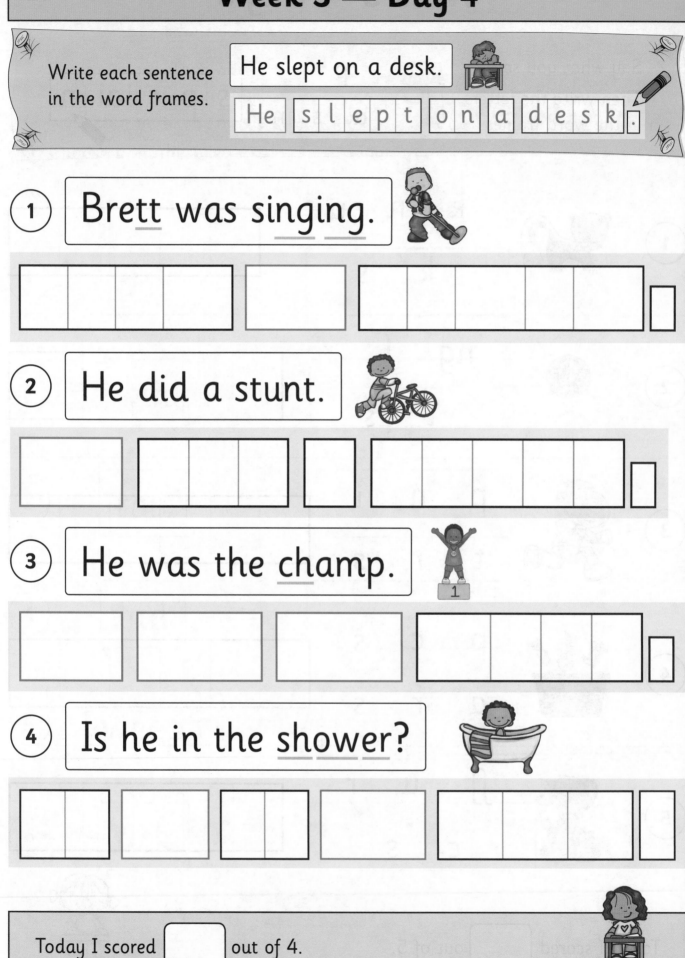

| He | s l e p t | o n | a | d e s k . |

1 Brett was singing.

2 He did a stunt.

3 He was the champ.

4 Is he in the shower?

Today I scored ☐ out of 4.

Week 3 — Day 5

Read each sentence. Draw a line to the best picture.

Look up there.

1 I like to crunch crisps.

2 We were freezing.

3 There were three scoops.

4 There is Jack Frost.

5 Were there straps on the bag?

Find and circle these words in the sentences.
like   there   were

Today I scored ⬚ out of 5.

Reception Phonics — Summer Term

Week 4 — Day 1

Read the word.
Then circle the correct picture.

land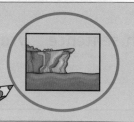

1 lift

2 yelp

3 bend

4 stink

5 point

6 next

7 tusks

8 Welsh

9 roast

10 growl

11 speech

12 brain

Today I scored ☐ out of 12.

Week 4 — Day 2

Read the word.
Then write a rhyming word in the word frame. The picture will help.

cramp 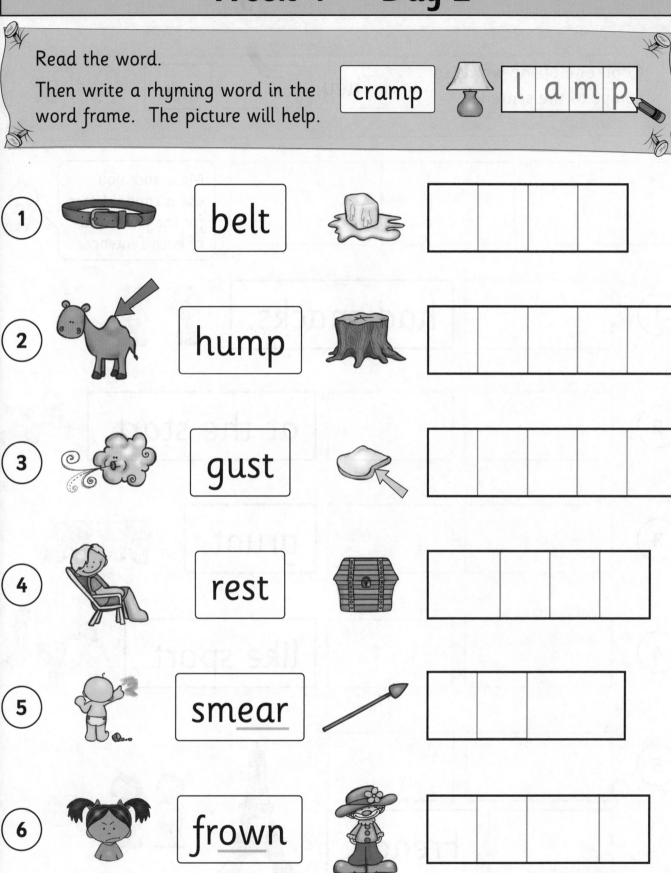 l a m p

1. belt

2. hump

3. gust

4. rest

5. s<u>me</u>ar

6. f<u>r</u>own

Today I scored [ ] out of 6.

Reception Phonics — Summer Term

Week 4 — Day 3

Copy one of the words to complete the sentence.

| They | are | lost. |

they   are   all

Make sure you use a capital letter for the first word of each sentence.

1 [ ] had snacks.

2 [ ] [ ] at the start.

3 [ ] [ ] grunt.

4 [ ] [ ] like sport.

5 [ ] [ ] [ ] French.

Today I scored [ ] out of 5.

Week 4 — Day 4

Write each sentence in the word frames.

Can you hear it?

| C a n | you | h ear | i t | ? |

1 Hug soft Ted.

2 She is painting.

3 She will help you.

4 You hunt for eggs.

Today I scored ☐ out of 4.

Reception Phonics — Summer Term

Week 4 — Day 5

Colour the picture that matches the sentence.

I went for a little jog.

 1 | It's so little. |

 2 | He has one tuft of hair. |

3 | Have one gift from me. |

4 | It's a little too steep. |

5 | I had one little chunk. |

6 | We kept one little pup. |

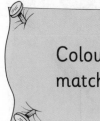 Find and circle these words in the sentences.
little   **one**

Today I scored ☐ out of 6.

Week 5 — Day 1

Add the ending. Then write the new word.

| fish | + | ing |

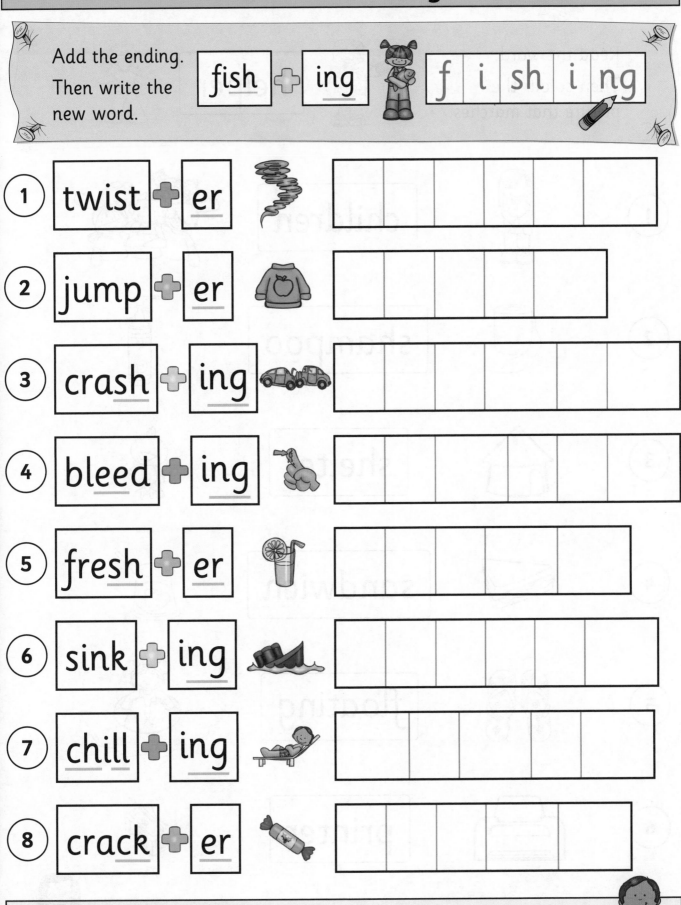

f | i | sh | i | ng

1. twist + er [ ][ ][ ][ ][ ][ ]

2. jump + er [ ][ ][ ][ ][ ][ ]

3. crash + ing [ ][ ][ ][ ][ ][ ][ ]

4. bleed + ing [ ][ ][ ][ ][ ][ ][ ]

5. fresh + er [ ][ ][ ][ ][ ][ ][ ]

6. sink + ing [ ][ ][ ][ ][ ][ ][ ]

7. chill + ing [ ][ ][ ][ ][ ][ ][ ]

8. crack + er [ ][ ][ ][ ][ ][ ][ ]

Today I scored [   ] out of 8.

Reception Phonics — Summer Term
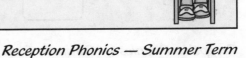

Week 5 — Day 2

Read the word.
Then colour the
picture that matches.

 helper

1  children

2 shampoo

3 shelter

4 sandwich

5 floating

6  printer

Today I scored ☐ out of 6.

Week 5 — Day 3

Copy one of the words to complete each sentence.

It's | my | plant.

 my   her

 Remember you will need to use a capital letter at the start of this word.

1 | fur is the softest.

2 I gulp | | drink.

3 She is in | | smart dress.

4 I bring | | lunch bag.

5 I can bend | | back.

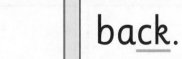
Today I scored [ ] out of 5.

Reception Phonics — Summer Term

Week 5 — Day 4

Write each sentence in the word frames.

They are wet.

| They | are | w | e | t | . |

1 They are sniffing.

| | | | | | | | |

2 Are they a p<u>air</u>?

| | | | | | |

3 They had lun<u>ch</u>.

| | | | | | | | | |

4 They are all br<u>ow</u>n.

| | | | | | | | |

Today I scored [ ] out of 4.

Week 5 — Day 5

Read each sentence and then draw a line to the best picture.

Do not run.

(1) We do not let the dog on the bed.

(2) What a me__ss__.

(3) I do not like __th__is __foo__d.

(4) Do not let go of me.

(5) You must do what I tell yo__u__.

Find and circle these words in the sentences.
do   what

Today I scored ☐ out of 5.

Reception Phonics — Summer Term

Week 6 — Day 1

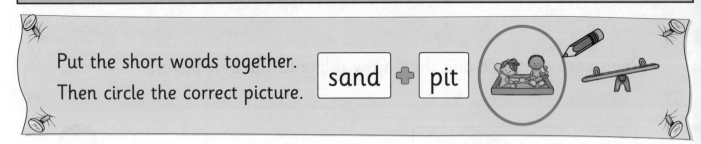

Put the short words together.
Then circle the correct picture.

sand + pit

(1) wind + mill

(2) hand + bag

(3) lip + stick

(4) gift + box

(5) moon + light

(6) sun + flower

Today I scored ☐ out of 6.

Week 6 — Day 2

Put the short words together.
Then write the new long word.

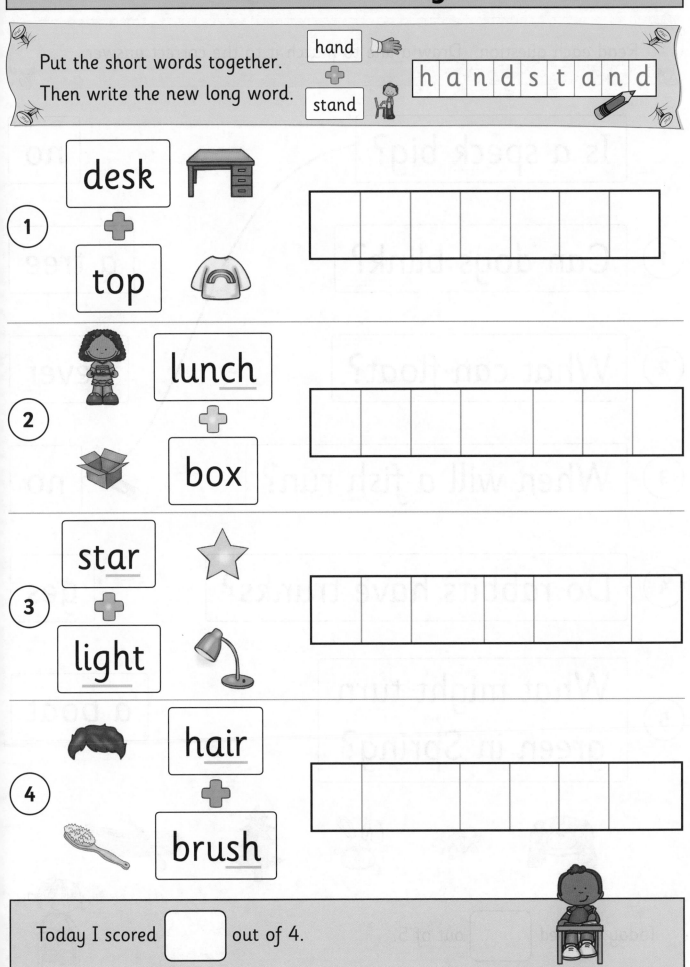

hand
➕
stand

| h | a | n | d | s | t | a | n | d |

1 desk ➕ top

| | | | | | | |

2 lunch ➕ box

| | | | | | |

3 star ➕ light

| | | | | | |

4 hair ➕ brush

| | | | | |

Today I scored [ ] out of 4.

Week 6 — Day 3

Read each question. Draw a line to match it to the correct answer.

Is a spe<u>ck</u> big?

no

(1) Can dogs blink?

a t<u>ree</u>

(2) What can fl<u>oa</u>t?

never

(3) When w<u>ill</u> a fi<u>sh</u> run?

no

(4) Do ra<u>bb</u>its have trunks?

yes

(5) What might t<u>ur</u>n gr<u>ee</u>n in Spri<u>ng</u>?

a b<u>oa</u>t

Today I scored [ ] out of 5.

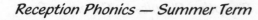

Reception Phonics — Summer Term

© CGP — Not to be photocopied

Week 6 — Day 4

Write the sentence in the word frames.

Her pet is brown.

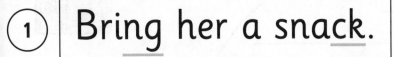 Her | p e t | i s | b r o w n | .

1 Bring her a snack.

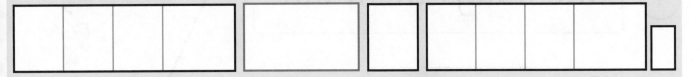

2 Grab my hand.

3 Her car is flash.

4 My back is stiff.

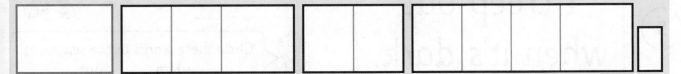

Today I scored ☐ out of 4.

Reception Phonics — Summer Term

Week 6 — Day 5

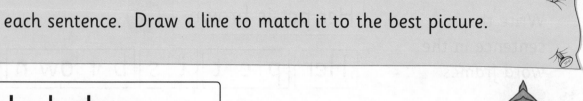

Read each sentence. Draw a line to match it to the best picture.

He helps out.

(1) She hangs them out.

(2) I can see out of the shelter.

(3) Cows sit down when it rains.

(4) He wept when he was tenth.

(5) I creep out when it's dark.

 Circle these words in the sentences.
when   **out**

Today I scored [ ] out of 5.

Week 7 — Day 1

Read the word.
Then circle the correct picture. | munch |

1 quickest

2 chimpanzee

3 charming

4 chopsticks

5 bricks

6 theft

7 froth

8 clock

Today I scored ☐ out of 8.

Reception Phonics — Summer Term

Week 7 — Day 2

Choose one of the sounds to complete the word.

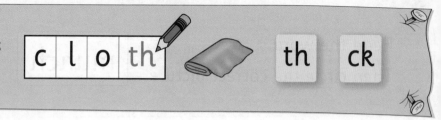

c l o th

th   ck

① s t i [ ] er   ck   th

② [ ] a m p i o n 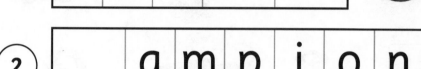   qu   ch

③ [ ] ur [ ]    th   ch

④ [ ] r o b   ck   th

⑤ d r e n [ ]   ch   ck

⑥ [ ] r o a t   qu   th

⑦ [ ] i l t    ch   qu

⑧ f l o [ ]   ck   ch

Today I scored [ ] out of 8.

Week 7 — Day 3

Say what you see.
Then write the letters
in the word frames.

l i
ck c

c | l | i | ck

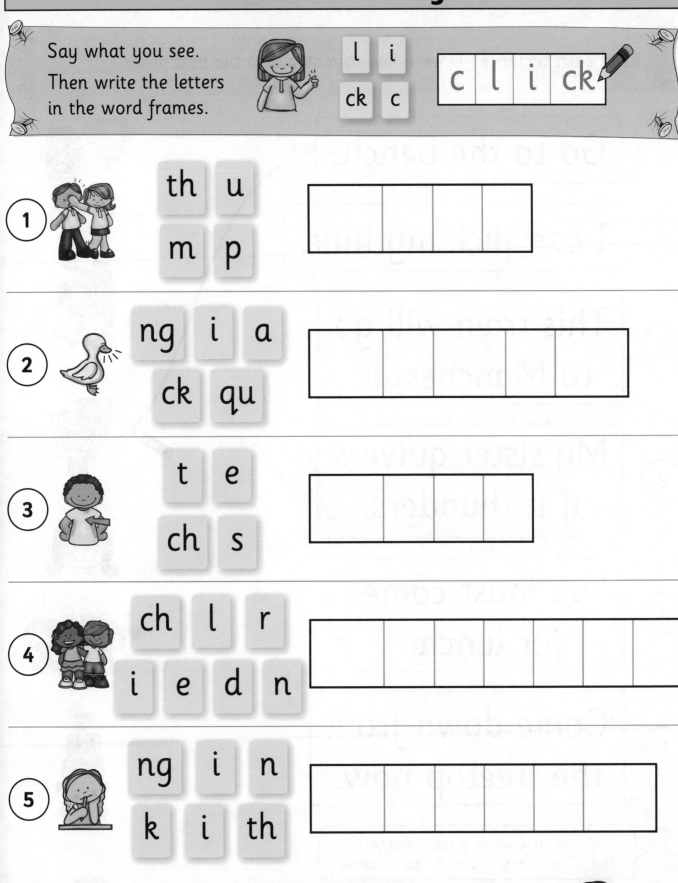

1. th u
    m p

2. ng i a
    ck qu

3. t e
    ch s

4. ch l r
    i e d n

5. ng i n
    k i th

Today I scored [ ] out of 5.

Week 7 — Day 4

Read each sentence. Draw a line to match it to the best picture.

Go to the bench.

(1) I can flick my hair.

(2) This train will go to Manchester.

(3) My sister quivers if it thunders.

(4) You must come for lunch.

(5) Come down from the treetop now.

Circle these words in the sentences.
the   to   my   you   go   come

Today I scored ☐ out of 5.

Week 7 — Day 5

Choose one of the words to complete the sentence.

Can | you | help me?

| go | to | my |
| the | you | come |

1 She steps on [ ] rocks.

2 Bella holds [ ] hand.

3 I went [ ] get a haircut.

4 Will [ ] drink this stuff?

5 We [ ] to chess club.

6 I [ ] from Mars.

Today I scored [ ] out of 6.

Reception Phonics — Summer Term

36

Week 8 — Day 1

Read the word and circle the correct picture.

starfish

1. goldfish

2. flash

3. shrimp

4. rubbish

5. twisting

6. melting

7. shivering

8. splashing

Today I scored [ ] out of 8.

Week 8 — Day 2

Choose a sound to complete each word.

| b | r | ai | n |

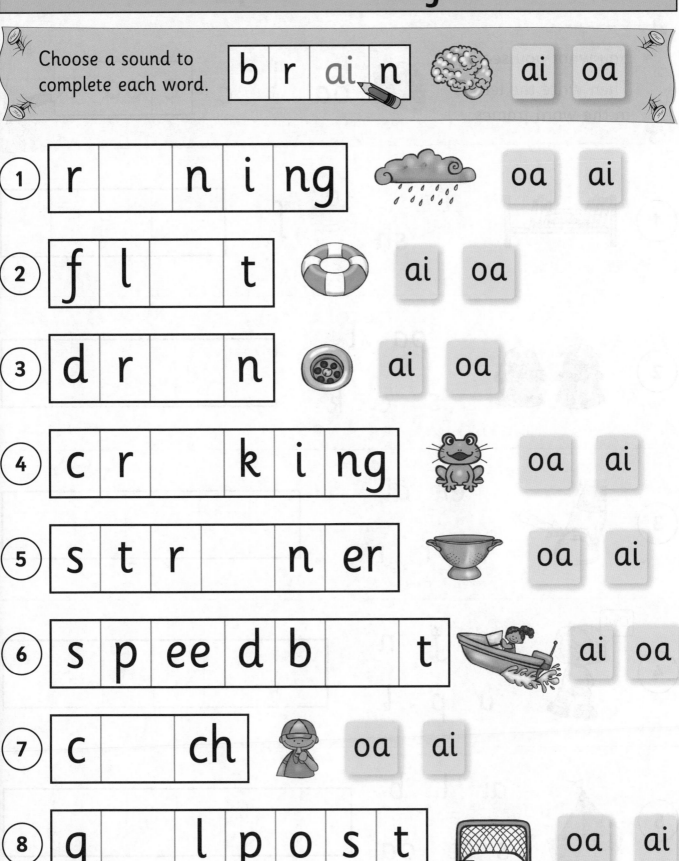

ai   oa

1. | r | | n | i | ng | oa   ai

2. | f | l | | t | ai   oa

3. | d | r | | n | ai   oa

4. | c | r | | k | i | ng | oa   ai

5. | s | t | r | | n | er | oa   ai

6. | s | p | ee | d | b | | t | ai   oa

7. | c | | ch | oa   ai

8. | g | | l | p | o | s | t | oa   ai

Today I scored ☐ out of 8.

Reception Phonics — Summer Term

Week 8 — Day 3

Say what you see.
Then write the letters
in the word frames.

oa l c   c | oa | l

1   l e f
      sh

2   oa l
    s c k

3   er ai
    t r n

4   ai f n
    u p l

5   ai l b
    s t oa

Today I scored ☐ out of 5.

Week 8 — Day 4

Read each question. Then circle the correct answer.

Is he flushing?  **yes** no

1. Was he blushing?  yes no

2. Have they got shorts on?  yes no

3. Can a shark get out onto land?  yes no

4. Did he have one fish in his net?  yes no

5. Is he helping out? yes no

 Find and circle these tricky words in the sentences.
they   have   he   was   one   out

Today I scored ☐ out of 5.

Week 8 — Day 5

Choose one of the tricky words to complete the sentence.

| Joan | was | sweeping. |

one   was   out

they   he   have

Make sure you use a capital letter for the first word of each sentence.

(1) She ____ planting an oak.

(2) Dev got ____ of the tent.

(3) ____ is not selfish.

(4) I ____ a gap in my teeth.

(5) ____ will finish the trail.

(6) It has ____ hump.

Today I scored [   ] out of 6.

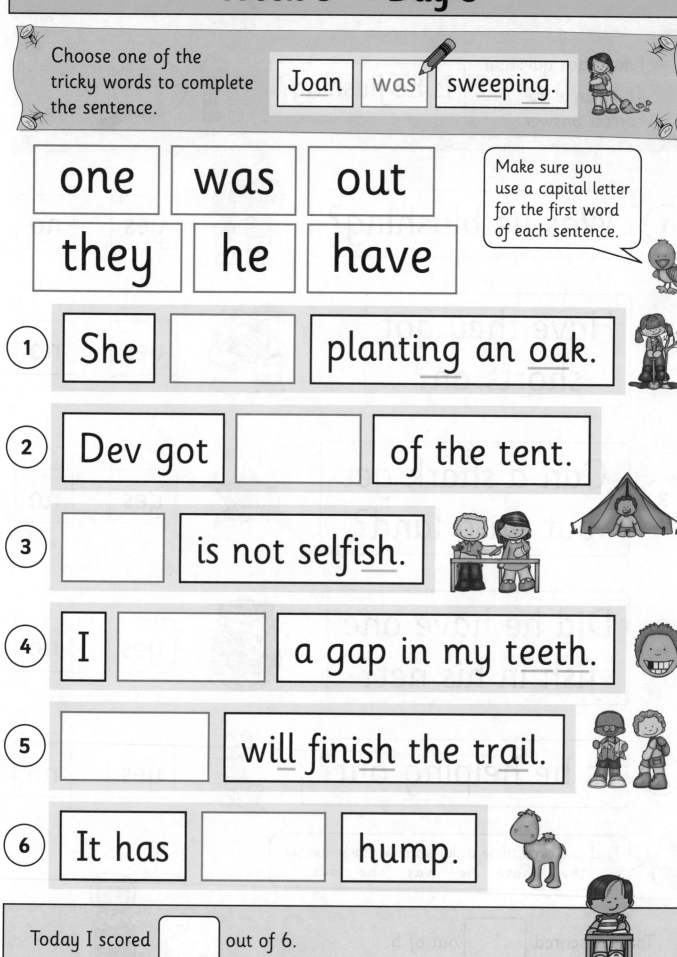

Week 9 — Day 1

Read the word.
Circle the correct picture.

boiling

1. looking

2. broomstick

3. feeding

4. beetroot

5. stool

6. igloo

7. scooter

8. bowing

Today I scored ☐ out of 8.

Week 9 — Day 2

Choose one of the sounds to complete the word.

g | ow | n

oo | ow

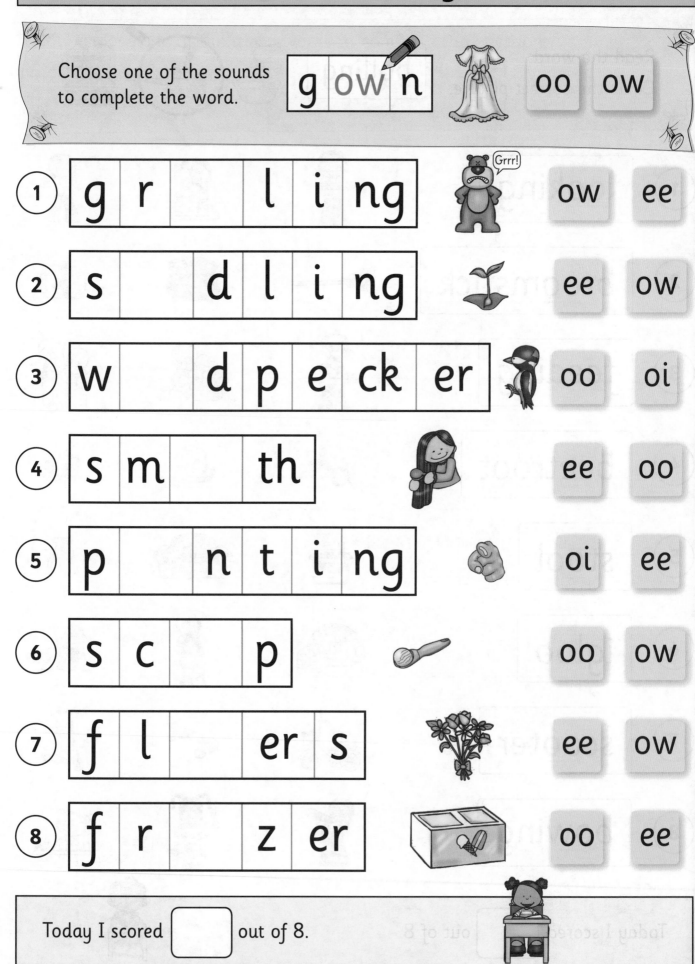

1. g r ☐ l i ng — ow | ee

2. s ☐ d l i ng — ee | ow

3. w ☐ d p e ck er — oo | oi

4. s m ☐ th — ee | oo

5. p ☐ n t i ng — oi | ee

6. s c ☐ p — oo | ow

7. f l ☐ er s — ee | ow

8. f r ☐ z er — oo | ee

Today I scored ☐ out of 8.

Week 9 — Day 3

Say what you see.
Then write the letters
in the word frames.

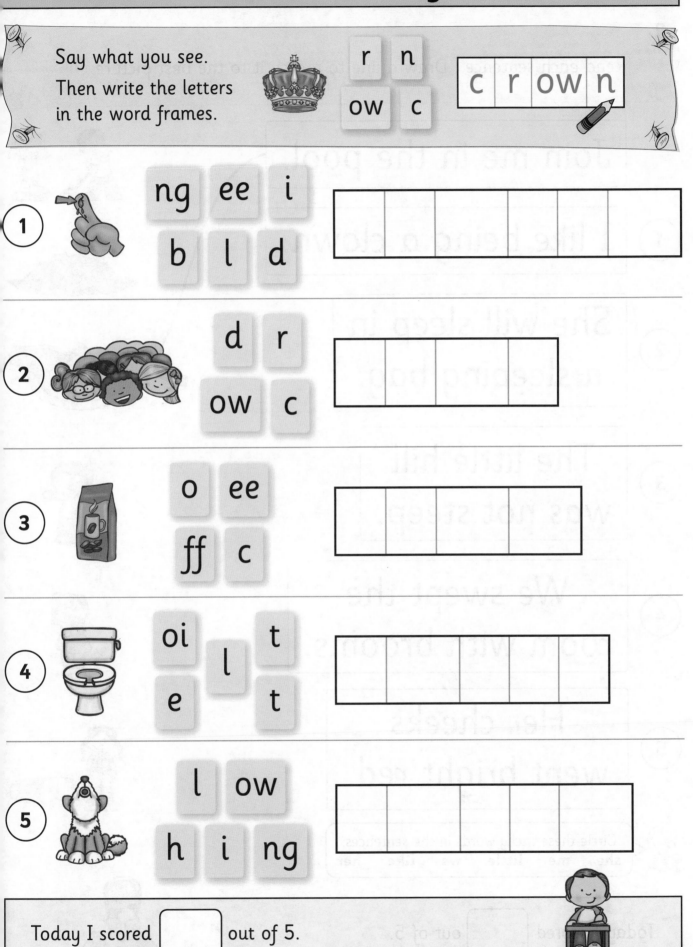

| r | n |
| ow | c |

| c | r | o | w | n |

1. | ng | ee | i |
   | b | l | d |

   | | | | | |

2. | d | r |
   | ow | c |

   | | | | |

3. | o | ee |
   | ff | c |

   | | | | |

4. | oi | l | t |
   | e | | t |

   | | | | |

5. | l | ow |
   | h | i | ng |

   | | | | | |

Today I scored ☐ out of 5.

Reception Phonics — Summer Term

44

Week 9 — Day 4

Read each sentence. Draw a line to match it to the best picture.

Join me in the pool.

(1) I like being a clown.

(2) She will sleep in a sleeping bag.

(3) The little hill was not steep.

(4) We swept the room with brooms.

(5) Her cheeks went bright red.

Circle these tricky words in the sentences.
she   me   little   we   like   her

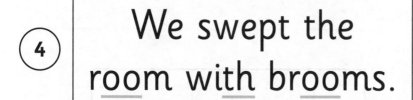

Today I scored [ ] out of 5.

Week 9 — Day 5

Choose one of the words to complete the sentence.

 She | shook her hand.

| like | me | she |
| little | we | her |

 Make sure you use a capital letter for the first word of each sentence.

1 He is big [ ] a tower.

2 The [ ] chicks cheep.

3 [ ] is pointing.

4 [ ] sit by Miss Cheema.

5 [ ] dress is brown.

6 Look at [ ] .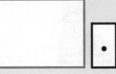

Today I scored [ ] out of 6.

Reception Phonics — Summer Term

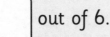

Week 10 — Day 1

Read the word and circle the correct picture.

scarf

1 burger

2 corner

3 start

4 stork

5 surfing

6 film star

7 toaster

8 bumper car

Today I scored ☐ out of 8.

Week 10 — Day 2

Choose a sound to complete the word.

| t | ur | n | i | p |

ar   ur

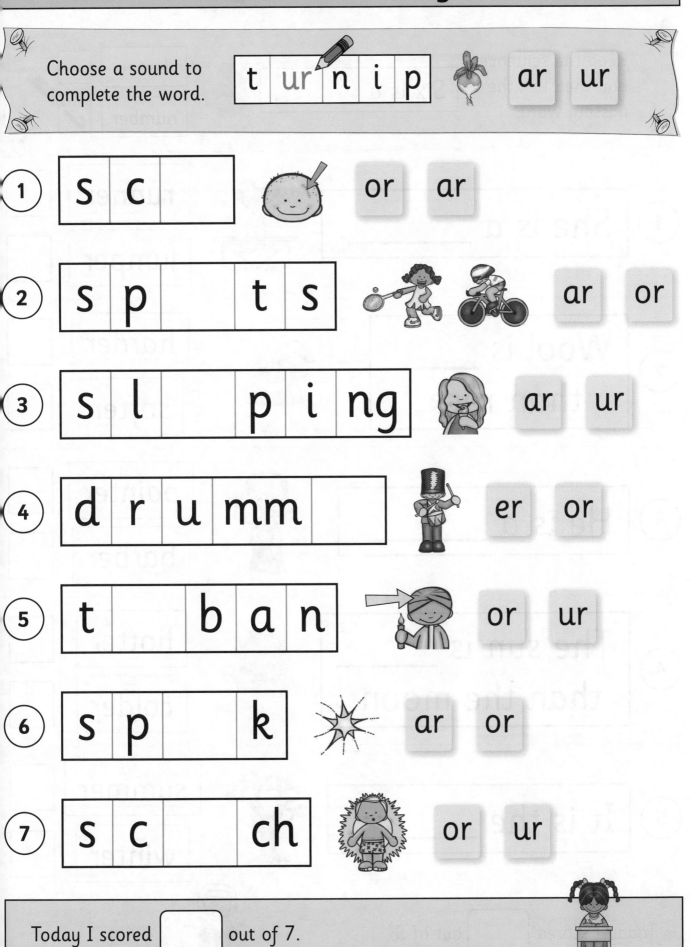

1. | s | c | | or   ar

2. | s | p | | t | s | ar   or

3. | s | l | | p | i | ng | ar   ur

4. | d | r | u | mm | | er   or

5. | t | | b | a | n | or   ur

6. | s | p | | k | ar   or

7. | s | c | | ch | or   ur

Today I scored [ ] out of 7.

Reception Phonics — Summer Term

Week 10 — Day 3

Read the sentence and then tick the missing word.

Six is a _____.

| letter | |
| number | ✔ |

1. She is a _____.

| runner | |
| jumper | |

2. Wool is ____ than rock.

| harder | |
| softer | |

3. He is a _____.

| painter | |
| barber | |

4. The sun is ____ than the moon.

| hotter | |
| colder | |

5. It is the _____.

| summer | |
| winter | |

Today I scored ☐ out of 5.

Week 10 — Day 4

Read the question and then tick the correct answer.

Are stars soft?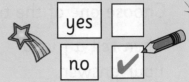

| yes | |
| no | ✔ |

---

1 Do balloons burst?

| yes | |
| no | |

---

2 When is it darker?

| morning | |
| midnight | |

---

3 What will dogs do in anger?

| snarl | |
| sleep | |

---

4 Can wood be burnt?

| yes | |
| no | |

---

5 What is a shark?

| plant | |
| animal | |

 Find and circle these tricky words in the sentences.
when   what   be   do

Today I scored ☐ out of 5.

Reception Phonics — Summer Term

Week 10 — Day 5

Choose one of the tricky words to complete the question.

Then tell a friend your answer. | Do | | pigs snort? |

| when | are | be |
| what | all | do |

Make sure you use a capital letter for the first word of each sentence.

1. [ ] | is the best sport?

2. [ ] | will we have lunch?

3. [ ] | you like skipping?

4. Do [ ] | flowers smell?

5. [ ] | you fond of frogs?

6. Can forks [ ] sharp?

Today I scored [ ] out of 6.

Week 11 — Day 1

Read the word and colour the correct picture.

flight

1 stairs

2 spear

3 manure

4 moonlight

5 airport

6 street light

Today I scored [ ] out of 6.

Reception Phonics — Summer Term

Week 11 — Day 2

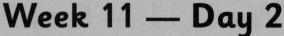

Choose a sound to complete the word.

s	e	c	ure

air · ure

1. | b | r | | t |

igh · air

2. | h | | b | a | n | d |

ear · air

3. | s | m | |

ure · ear

4. | m | a | t | |

ure · igh

5. | f | u | n | f | |

igh · air

6. | s | t | ar | l | | t |

ear · igh

7. | c | l | |

ear · ure

Today I scored ☐ out of 7.

Week 11 — Day 3

Say what you see.
Then write the letters
in the word frames.

n a
air m

air | m | a | n

1

igh
h er

2

ure
d c

3

f r
t igh

4

d b
ear s

5

t n s
l igh u

Today I scored ☐ out of 5.

Reception Phonics — Summer Term

Week 11 — Day 4

Read the sentence.
Then draw a
picture to match.

There were no sweets left.

1 I said no to the dog.

2 There were some flowers
and trees in the park.

Find and circle these tricky words in the sentences.
I   some   were   there   said   no

Today I scored ☐ out of 2.

Week 11 — Day 5

Choose one of the tricky words to complete the sentence.

No | food or drinks.

I | some | said | there | no | were

1. [ ] standing on the toilet.

2. [ ] sang on a log.

3. We [ ] planting a tree.

4. He [ ] yes.

5. She has [ ] pom poms.

6. It's cold out [ ] .

Today I scored [ ] out of 6.

Reception Phonics — Summer Term

Week 12 — Day 1

Read the word.
Then circle the correct picture.

dress

1 cliff

2 frills

3 press

4 coffee

5 fizz

6 handcuffs

7 windmill

8 smelling

Today I scored [ ] out of 8.

Reception Phonics — Summer Term   © CGP — Not to be photocopied

Week 12 — Day 2

Choose a sound to complete each word.

| s | n | i | ff | s |

| ss | ff | ll |

---

1 | b | l | e | | | **ff** | **ll** | **ss**

---

2 | s | p | e | | | **zz** | **ff** | **ll**

---

3 | f | r | i | | | **ll** | **zz** | **ff**

---

4 | s | p | i | | | **ss** | **ll** | **zz**

---

5 | a | c | r | o | |  | **ff** | **ss** | **ll**

---

6 | g | r | i | | i | n | g | | **ll** | **ff** | **ss**

---

7 | s | c | r | u | | | **ff** | **zz** | **ll**

---

8 | ear | m | u | | | **ss** | **ff** | **zz**

Today I scored [   ] out of 8.

Reception Phonics — Summer Term

Week 12 — Day 3

Put a line under the two letters in the word that make one sound.

crash

 You have practised all of the sounds in these words, so now **you** can underline them yourself.

(1) **bricks**

(2) **stiff**

(3) **groom**

(4) **bench**

(5) **swings**

(6) **skill**

(7) **screen**

(8) **smart**

(9) **grain**

(10) **crown**

Today I scored [ ] out of 10.

Reception Phonics — Summer Term

© CGP — Not to be photocopied

Week 12 — Day 4

Circle the word that has **more than one** sound made of two letters.

shell  bell

1. quill jazz

2. drums shark

3. roasting drop

4. freezer green

5. drip torch

6. crack quick

Today I scored ____ out of 6.

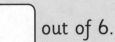

Week 12 — Day 5

Practise writing these tricky words.

1. do

2. go

3. she

4. was

5. are

6. like

7. said

8. they

9. have

10. little

11. what

12. some

13. there

14. were

Today I scored _____ out of 14.